...and then *you're alive!*

Notebook

...and then *you're alive!*

Copyright © 2013 Jim Rai
www.atydbook.com

A catalogue record for this book is available from the British Library

Published 2013 by Compass Publishing

ISBN 978-1-907308-28-4

Set by The Book Refinery Ltd
Printed in the United Kingdom by Berforts Press Ltd

Dedication

I dedicate this to you...

Introduction

The idea behind the creation of this notebook was to allow you the reader, to reflect on the direction ahead.

After you have taken in the 47 thoughts set out in... *and then you're dead!*, you have a choice - you can either put the book on the shelf and leave it there, or you can give it life by reflecting on your own personal experiences and where you find yourself today. I very much hope that you use this notebook to help lend some perspective as to how you go forward from here in the time you have left.

I wish you the very best and that you take the opportunity to enjoy the rest of your journey.

1

How many summers do you have left to go? Take a guess...

Don't take life so seriously as we are only visitors here for a short time.

2

Two Categories of People – Which one do you fall Into?

If you had a choice, would you choose to be a person who is known for his/her positive outlook to life or for his/her negative one?

3

The 70% rule

Try to aim for at least a 70% positive day by adopting a forward and confident attitude to your life and relationships. However, do not beat yourself up over it if you don't quite get there, after all you are human, and all human beings have some negative thoughts and times of indecision.

4

Too much thinking – relax!

Stop thinking too much and too deeply, you'll run yourself into the ground! Not all questions have an answer, move on!

5

No more excuses!

You may well say, "Easier said than done Jim! You don't have an abusive or intimidating partner, a bullying boss or colleague, an unruly child or nagging parents..." the list goes on. In fact, I have known people who have had to deal with all four of these types of negative relationships, and the only way they overcame them was by taking positive steps to bring about change. They actually did something rather than complain about it, that was the difference.

6

Life is life – fight for it

7

You and your relationships

My eldest brother has developed the habit of complaining about the world continually letting him down. I often ask him "Why do you have such high expectations of people in the first place? Is it them or is it you who is at fault?"

8

It's your journey

We are all on our own journey – don't compare it with others – just try to enjoy yours! Do not judge another's path, as you have no idea of the journey they've had to endure.

9

A little bit of love goes a long, long way

Whatever you do, do it with love. You make a living by what you earn, you make a life by what you give.

10

Laugh and be happy

Just for a few minutes, allow your mind to wander back to a day when someone or something made you really happy, and you laughed naturally without feeling you had to. What was it that made you smile?

11

Keep it simple

*The best things in life come in the form of simplicity
through children and relationships*

12

Health is true wealth

When we see people who train, look fit and eat healthy, we often say,
"It would be great to be like that, but it's way too much hassle."

13

Let them talk

It's none of your business what others think of you!

14

Do you know your weaknesses?

Every one of us have weaknesses, but many of us don't like to admit them, not even to ourselves – that is the worrying bit!

15

Where are the crutches?

Your body and mind are stronger than you think.

16

Take advantage of your strengths

We all have strengths, some of which we are aware of and others of which we are not. Be resourceful with your strengths.

17

Your happiness rests with you

"Happiness is a bit like a butterfly..." and is determined by your attitude, not your accomplishments.

18

At times do you feel all alone?

Mother Teresa once said, "Being unwanted, unloved, uncared for or forgotten, is a much greater hunger and a much greater poverty than the person who has nothing to eat."

19

Look forward to one thing each day

A simple way of getting some meaning into your life is to devote yourself to creating something that gives you purpose and meaning each day.

20

The London cab driver

It is all about perspective!

21

Only one set of shoulders – easy on the weight

We only have one set of shoulders, and there is only so much weight we can carry on them.

22

Congratulations! You have won the lottery

I believe you have won the lottery each day, you just don't know it!

23

Give with *your* hands

The gift of giving with your own hands cannot be measured.

24

Life's special moments

*Capture those special moments with those special people in an
imaginary glass bottle – they're worth their weight in gold.*

25

Just set some goals, any will do, but just do it please

Don't just follow your dreams – chase them!

26

The virtues of garlic, ginger, chilli, lemon & turmeric

Yes, I am of Indian origin, and no I don't have shares in the agriculture industry relating to any of these foods!

27

Same old...day in, day out

Stuck in a rut? Tired of the same journey into work? Eating the same food? Following the same routine everyday?

28

Remember to lead by example

We sometimes forget our roles or positions in life. We tend to go through it forgetting that others may be relying on us and looking towards us for guidance.

29

Blue sky time

Try a bit of 'blue-sky' time in the morning before you start your day.

30

Family peace conference

A family conference once in a while is no bad thing.

31

Parlez–vous français?

Come on, at least try to make an attempt at learning each other's language.

32

Play, rewind and pause – press play

Try if you can, to stop pressing the rewind button, as it slows down what could be a great movie inspired by a true-life story.

33

The amazing healing qualities of time

All the words, people, love, comfort and support in the world will never come close to the healing qualities that time provides.

34

The three faces

Contrary to popular opinion (and science), every person possesses three separate faces.

35

Win yourself and you will win the world

Before you can achieve your aspirations and goals, you need to have a profound understanding of yourself.

36

Ego meet humility – arrogance meet intelligence

Don't make ego or self-belief your drivers, control and steer them on an even keel.

37

Box clever

"Remember, living in favourable and unfavourable situations is a part of life, but smiling in all those situations is the art of life." ~ *Source unknown*

38

It's not the place, it's the people

For over 25 years I've always made time to meet up at least once a week with my brothers and friends, to share and catch up on the weeks highs and lows.

39

What is the true test when measuring your success?

Success is best measured not by the value of your bank balance, but by the balance you have achieved in your life.

40

Character over gifting

Everyone wants to ensure that his or her children are provided with the best education and are given the best opportunities in order to excel in their chosen field...but we need to question is this the only education they require?

41

The best anti-ageing product

I call it the 'Benjamin Button' potion - someone who gains his youth as each year passes.

42

Say it before it's too late, while you still can

Don't leave it too late, as you may well regret it!

43

The key elements to a meaningful life

A wonderful person I met many years ago, called Bonnie Katsumoto expressed her thoughts on what a meaningful life meant to her, for which I'm grateful;

44

One's nature and one's habit

Two different beasts – one is what you are stuck with, like it or not, the other is created and can be changed.

45

The orchard of life

Your flowers have been well taken care of but do you really want them to flourish in a desert.

46

Forgiveness – a beautiful gift you give to yourself

It never fails to amaze me how unforgiving we've become. We lack the gift of tolerance, make judgements too hastily, and look for someone to blame too quickly.

47

The 14–year life certificate

This is my gift to you – a 14 - year life certificate.

Your companion notes

Your companion notes

Your companion notes

Your companion notes

Your companion notes

Your companion notes

Your companion notes

Your companion notes

Your companion notes

Your companion notes

Your companion notes

Your companion notes